This Issue...

FLEATURES

Pussweek Issue Five
Created, written, designed and produced by Bexy McFly.
Special thanks to Ciro Figaro, Vanessa Watson, Mel Sorini, Wenee Yap, Alf Santomingo, Brooke Jacobs, and RSPCA Qld.

This book is dedicated to Noob and Trim, the greatest black cats to ever steal my soul.

TOP 10

Foolproof* ways

to become a

SCARY CAT

(as opposed to the pathetic pussy you are meow)

Trim

H ullo there sports fans! This issue is all about creepy stuff, and we all know there's nobody creepier than ...well, Fred. But lucky for you, I'm here! Me, black cat extraordinaire, Trim! And this issue I've teamed up with the countdown crew to devise the top ten spookiest stunts EVER! So, BEWARE! These sports are not for the soft of paw, and they're designed especially for black cats. You can still do them if you're not black, you'll just look like a stupid dork and black cats will make fun of you. And if you fail (which you surely might), you could die and come back as a zombie. But try not to, because zombies are gross and they suck at sports.

KEY: 🐈 Fright factor 🌙 Difficulty 🐾 Risk

10 Basically anything involving a pumpkin 🐈🐈🐈🐈

WHAT? Humans think pumpkins are scary for some reason. Morons.

YOU WILL NEED: One or more pumpkins.

HOW: All you have to do is just hang out near/on/in one or more of said pumpkins, and try to look creepy. Fright factor greatly increases if you're a black cat (for colourist bigots).

9 Classic Face-Pull

🐈🐈🐈🌙🌙

HUH? Depending on your face, this can be quite terrifying.

YOU WILL NEED: One face.

HOW: Make your face as scary as possible. Suggested moves include baring your teef, hissing, and sticking out your tongue (see left).

8 The Conjuring
🐈 🐈 🐈 🐈 🐈 🐈

WAIT, WHAT? Yep.

YOU WILL NEED: At least one eye; a solid stare; inner demons; absolute stillness.

METHOD: Go somewhere random, then literally just sit there and switch on your eye(s). That's it. Oh, and release a few demons while you're at it. Let them stretch their legs, they deserve it.

Model: Megs Image: Thomas Esamie

7 Ground Attack
🐈 🐈 🐈 🐾 🐾 ☠

THIS IS WHAT? Simple and effective.

HOW: Sit on the ground and wait for someone to come walking by. When they get close, jump up on your hind legs and stick your paws up (see above pic). Victim will be terrified and die of shock.

6 Aerial Attack
🐈 🐈 🐈 🐈 🐾 🐾 ☠ ☠

WHAT IS THIS? The best fun ever.

HOW: Find a good vantage point (i.e. a roof or tree). Perch yourself there and wait for an approaching victim. When you have a clear shot at their head, launch yourself toward them, and dig in.

5 Mysterious Crap Circles
🐈 🐈 🐈 🐈 🐈

HUH? Crap circles are strange patterns that appear mysteriously overnight, sometimes in farmers' fields. They provoke puzzlement, intrigue, and they creep everybody out. They've been studied for decades, but the question remains: Who – or what – is making them? Well, I'll tell you. We are.

METHOD: Wait until everybody is asleep, then poop in delicate formation in strange spots around the back yard. The more detailed and precise, the more effective they'll be.

4 Get your prick on

HUH? Never underestimate the shock factor of an unforeseen prick.

YOU WILL NEED: Extremely sharp claws. And I'm not talking about your everyday pointers here. You're gonna need an all-in-one buffer & polisher for this. We suggest the Kitska wall scratcher (left, available at kitska.com.au) because it lets you stretch & warm up at the same time.

MODUS OPERANDI: Sharpen every day for several weeks. Avoid the trimmers at all costs. Then, sit where your human/dog/bird/lizard/other would-be victim can see you, and swiftly and dramatically draw your swords (yes, at this point they will be swords). You won't even need to use them, just sit there licking them while making eye contact, and your opponent will be so scared they'll do a little wee.

▲ Warm up & sharpen in style!

▲ Have you ever seen anything more terrifying? No. You have not.

3 Extreme Shedding

WHAT? Did you know that we have the power to make humans horribly ill? Did you know that some humans are allergic to our fur, and just being near a few strands could take them down, probably possibly sort of maybe killing them? Well it's true.

YOU WILL NEED:
- Fur (the more the better).
- Fake smooching skills *(see Pussweek Issue #3 - Putting the mooch in smooch).*

HOW: For best results it's recommended that you purrpare well, saving up your winter coat and purrforming this particular sport in Summer or Spring. Start by making yourself warm, then let the shedding process do its thing. Try to shake off your excess follicles and spread them evenly all over the house. Then, get close to your chosen victim, and rub yourself on their face, paying special attention to the nose. Sit on them if you have to.

WARNING: Retreat to safety and find cover before the convulsive sneezing begins. You don't need that noise.

CLAWTION: Excessive shedding causes baldness.

▲ Good technique

▲ The side-prize: A bountiful booty

▲ You're doing it wrong

2 Ride a Broomstick

THIS IS WHAT?
Brooms are famous the world over as the transpor
mode of choice for black cats and their witch slaves
But did you know they also collect and eat valuable
treasure? Well, they do.

YOUR MISSION:
Your mission is three-fold:

Fold 1: To battle the broom for the ultimate side
prize: Fluff and dust and dirt n' crap.

Fold 2: Broomsticks are essential for black cats in
spooky situations, so you must conquer this bristlec
beast and steal its soul so you can eventually take i
for a joyride (and be scary).

Fold 3: Take it for a joyride (and be scary).

RECOMMENDED FOR:
Cats who've had it up to here with smug broomy
jerks and, well, the minutiae of life in general. This
activity is also good for scaring humans and looking
cool in front of your bowl.

METHOD:
Step 1
When the broom wakes up (this happens withou
warning, so be ready), it will start rapidly swaying
back and forth on the floor because it is possessec
by Satan. Be brave, make eye contact, and initiate
butt-wiggle.

Step 2
Pounce. If you do this propurrly, the broom wil
vomit and all of its valuable bounty (a.k.a. soul) wil
spread far and wide.

Step 3
Play in regurgitated dirt n' crap for a while.

Step 4
Grab hold of those bristles and hold on for dear lives
Then ride like the wind! Don't forget to pull a ver
scary face (see #9: Classic Face-Pull).

CLAWTION:
Broom may fight back. Use you
best judgement and, when tha
doesn't work, leg it. If you're
scared, start by practicing or
a small training broom to build
your confidence (left).

◀ Practicing on a training broom will
help you be less of a pussy

Meowloween Arch

YOUR MISSION:
To look terrifying and scare everyone.

NUMBER **#1**

WHY?
Black cats have a reputation to uphold. That reputation is heavy and requires a strong, flexible back that can contort into an intimidating arch which will be sturdy enough to support your greatness. What does this mean, you ask? We're not sure. Shut up.

HOW?
Arching is more difficult than it looks. It's not just about a simple back-bend – there are several dimensions to an effective arch:

- **Fur -** Your fur needs to stand at attention. NO FLACCID FOLLICLES! A single limp strand can destroy your savage appearance. Long-haired cats have a huge advantage here.

- **Height & Pitch -** Your arch needs to be as high as possible and consistent throughout. Many cats have a tendency to start out strong, then let their butts go floppy. There is nothing terrifying about a floppy butt. Unless your name is Fred.

- **Body Size -** The bigger you are, the more successful you'll be. If you're petite, this is where long hair and a high arch come in especially handy to create an optical illusion of grandeur and big scary scariness.

- **Facial Expression -** There's no point having a rockin' body if your face sucks. Open your mouth, show your fangs, and hiss repeatedly. For extra points, make some weird noises too, including that throat growly thing.

- **Tail -** Not knowing what to do with your tail is quite common in this situation. The trick is to keep the curve going. Make your tail continue your body's hard work and get a sweet butt-curl going. Your tail fur has more spike-potential than the rest of your body, so make it count. Plus, we all know black cats have the biggest tails. **PW**

▲ Purrfect execution. Good face.

▲ Tail must be close to the body, and intensely bushy

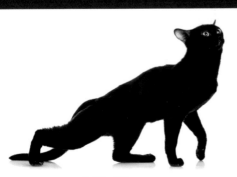

▲ What? No.

▲ Still no.

QUIZ

Is your
HUMAN a
WITCH?
...OR JUST A COLOSSAL JERK?

Wooo-oo, witch-ay human... They've got your moon in their eyes when you wake them up with your behind... But how do you know if your human is a regular boring one, or if their idiotic behaviour is a sign of something more sinister? Well, surprise, surprise! Pussweek has the answers! As will you, when you educate yourself by taking this handy quiz. A word of advice, though: Do this in a safe place. Take a piece of garlic with you. But don't lick it. Or smell it. Or talk to it. You know what? Forget what we said about the garlic. It's not worth it. Just lay low. Or don't. It doesn't matter.

How would you describe your human's appearance?

Kind of funny looking.

Unwashed, unkempt, crazy hair, and a questionable scent.

Clean and tidy, well groomed – surprisingly normal (for a human).

Not sure - I try my best not to look at them.

What kinds of foods does your human shovel into your bowl?

The usual: eye of newt, tail of rat, toe of frog, that sort of thing.

The same friggen kibble every friggen day.

Standard issue meat or fish.

Whatever I command.

What kind of activities do you catch your human partaking in?

They fill a huge tub with boiling water, light several candles, take off all their coverings and then soak their weird naked bodies in said water while drinking a blood-like substance from a glass goblet.

They have an obsession with the broomstick and seem to enjoy pushing it around the house for no reason, possibly working up the courage to ride it.

Once a year they murder a pumpkin, rip its brains out, then light a fire in its head and leave it on the doorstep – presumably as a warning to other pumpkins.

I literally give zero f**ks what my human does at any time. Ever.

Has your human ever tried to involve you in any of their weird rituals?

They made eye contact with me once. That was pretty awkward.

They once mentioned something about going for a walk outside, then they held me down, forcedly strapped me in to a weird apparatus with a leash attached, and then dragged me around in a circle instead. It was messed up.

They consistently expect me to care about them. They are consistently disappointed.

They woke me up once. Once.

You discover that your human has an aversion to garlic. What do you do?

Go out and collect a butt load of garlic from the nearest garden.

Roll over and go back to sleep.

Make a plan to find out what garlic is, and very nearly see it through.

Wonder why valuable space in your brain is being taken up by this useless information.

6. Does your human ever wear a pointy hat?

a) No. They have no sense of style.

b) Yes. They have no sense of style.

c) I don't know and I don't care.

d) If they do, I've peed in it.

7. Which of the following behaviours have you noticed from your human?

a) While sleeping, their eyes flicker and they speak in tongues.

b) They get together with other humans and make strange cackling noises.

c) They eat lettuce without gagging.

d) Notice? Human? Please.

8. Last time you were sick, what did your human do?

a) Transported you straight to Satan's Lair, a.k.a. the vet.

b) Held your gob open and shoved a concoction of pills and grossness down your throat.

c) Fussed over you until you threw up.

d) Yelled at you for puking in their shoe.

Your scores

	a)	b)	c)	d)
1.	a) 6	b) 9	c) 3	d) 0
2.	a) 3	b) 6	c) 9	d) 0
3.	a) 6	b) 9	c) 3	d) 0
4.	a) 3	b) 9	c) 6	d) 0
5.	a) 9	b) 3	c) 6	d) 0
6.	a) 6	b) 9	c) 0	d) 3
7.	a) 9	b) 6	c) 3	d) 0
8.	a) 9	b) 6	c) 3	d) 0

0 - 23: WHO-MAN?

Your priorities are in purrfect order. You know that as long as your bowl is full, it doesn't matter if your human is a witch or a jerk or anything in between, and you'll be damned if you're going to waste your valuable time worrying about it.

24 - 47: LAME-O

Your human is lame. No witch, no jerk. Just an average, boring Lamey McLameface.

48 - 64: WITCH!

Don't be scared. See if you can get your paws on a hammer and a couple of two-by-fours.

65 - 72: JERK

Look. Your human is a jerk. There are no two ways about it. The best thing to do is be a jerk right back. Yeah! It'll be a battle of the jerks! A proper, good old fashioned jerk-off! Wait, that can't be right...

PW

My gross
Affliction

with Fred Little

Well, here we are. Part two of My Gross Affliction: The not-so-social experiment where I, **Fred Little**, willingly present myself before Satan (or the vet, whatever you wanna call it), and sacrifice my incredibly fine body to pokes, prods and probes, all in the name of journalism.

This issue we delve a little deeper. So deep, in fact, that what was meant to be a routine temperature test took a dark turn and ended up being its own dark, cavernous horror story. But that's a tale for another page.

For now, sit back, relax, and enjoy as I tell you about gross things.

So you're
itchy a.f.

L isten, we've all been there: You go out, you meet a nice cat, you get along well. You roll around in the grass for a while and you both have a great time. Then a day later you develop a mysterious itch.

One annoying little tickle becomes one HUGE irritation, and before long you can't even nap propurrly without waking up to scratch and gum at your fur every eight and a half seconds. You curse the cat who infected you with this parasite - they didn't even have the courtesy to warn you first.

You vow never to play with a stranger, or to have unplanned fun ever again. You're ashamed of your bad decisions. You fall into a deep depression. You begin to chew your own fur off. Soon you're choking on hairballs as big as your head and you're furiously trying to manoeuvre the pathetic strands of fur you have left in a feeble effort cover your bald patches.

Your self confidence is shattered. You let yourself go. You drink some clotted cream. You lose all self control, pee where you shouldn't, and then earn yourself a smack-bottom. You stumble upon some catnip, you're overcome by paranoia, then you freak out and escape. But there's nowhere to go and you don't know where you are so you wander the streets. You become a stray. You start exposing your belly in return for food, and you can't remember the last time you felt the warm embrace of a skirting board against your cheek.

You wither away, mangy and still burning with that eternal itch - a constant, painful reminder of that day you threw caution to the wind and lost your head. And for what? Was it even worth it, you ask? No. No, it most certainly was not. What have you become? A FLEA BAG, that's what.

Yes, it's true - we've all been there. And I think we can all agree it's better to live without these hitchhiking, vampiric jerk fleas and just avoid the drama, am I right? Yes. Yes, I am.

Fleas & thank you

EWW.

Eww is correct. Fleas are tiny bugs that nom on your skin and make you itch like a motherfluffer. They suck – both literally and figuratively – but thankfully, they're destructible and preventable.

The subtle hints of rabbit and fishy undertones in this vintage cat's blood are reminiscent of the Burmese terroir, don't you agree?

Indeed

▲ **Fig. 1.1** The cat flea, a.k.a. ctenocephalides felis, a.k.a. stupidis jerkis, is the most common creep of all.

Flea Symptoms:

- You're insanely itchy
- You scratch a lot
- Everything sucks
  (more than usual)
- Everything's annoying
  (more than usual)

Treatment:

- A less than delicious tablet
  to obliterate said fleas
- Hissing and frustrated licks
- Prevention

MEH, WHAT'S THE WORST THAT COULD HAPPEN?

Listen, we've all been there: A flea finds its way onto your luscious fur and takes a little swill on your finely ripened blood. He likes what he tastes, invites his friends round for cocktail night, and those friends invite more friends. Before long, it's an epic party and you're the host. And just like any good host, you're not having any fun. Hey, look! That first flea met another flea and now they're starting a family. Their babies are growing up so fast and they're planning a big family trip to your left ear next summer. Yes, it's true. We've all been there. The left ear is a wonderful spot.

Left to their own devices, fleas can cause serious damage. Not only will they trash the joint and suck up enough of your blood to give you anemia, scratching them can lead to gross open sores and even more gross infections, and an especially gross trip (or twelve) to STV (Satan The Vet).

I'M BIT!! I'M FREAKIN' BIT!! WHAT MEOW?!

First things first: Cry. When that's done, rub yourself all over your human's bed, clothes, towels and food. The power is in your paws because you can actually pass the fleas on to your human, giving them the gift of irritation.

If you've already felt the pinch, take a Flea Knockdown tablet - It'll wipe out the colony of creeps like wildfire. Then command your human slave to dab some Flea Control on the back of your neck every once in a while - this will stop the fleas' successors from returning for another go.

PURINA TOTAL CARE (below) is especially good because if you get rained on it won't wash off. However, if you're the type of cat who gets rained on, fleas probably aren't your biggest problem right meow.

So you think your sh*t don't
stink?
Bruh, it sorta does...

Gross Affliction #4: ATOMIC POOP

Sorry to be the one to tell you this, but not everything we do is immaculate and salutary. How do I know this? Because I followed Ollie into the bathroom once. It wasn't pretty. The guy is basically a walking gas chamber. He's like a rotten sea-bass: Beautiful and appealing on the outside, but fermented and possibly deadly on the inside. Myself and the Pussweek team worked tirelessly for literally seconds to cover up that stank, but in the end we had to admit defeat and run fast-paced laps of the office to lose the stench.

Well, maybe that's just Ollie, I hear you say. No, it's not just Ollie, OK? I myself am ashamed to admit that I've been caught short a few times by my own rank perfume. And who among us can say that they have never taken a whiff of their own leavings and almost gagged? That's why we cover it up so fastidiously, and why we wait for our human slaves to come home before we do it so they can shovel it out immediately. Duh.

Nevertheless, it isn't easy to come to terms with the fact that your poop stinks. It's embarrassing. It's degrading. It's like declaring that you're not purrfect, which, clearly, we all are. How dare our poop give us away? Damn disrespectful pieces of crap...

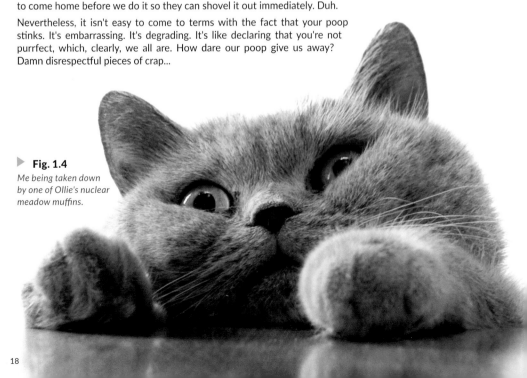

▶ **Fig. 1.4**
Me being taken down by one of Ollie's nuclear meadow muffins.

◄ *Does your crap pass the sniff test?*

WHY DOES MY POOP STINK?

There are many reasons why your back end expulsions might be less than pleasing to the nostril. Let's look at a few:

WHAT ARE YOU EATING? Sometimes the food you eat can make your poop smell worse. This is no reason to cut out the foods you love, but remember: a minute on the chops could mean an hour on the box.

ARE YOU SICK? An upset tummy could contribute to a toxic litter tray. Stay hydrated, rest, and try not to be sick anymore, mmmkay?

ARE YOU OLD? It's a known fact that the older you are, the more you stink. Just look at humans.

ARE YOU JUST NATURALLY STINKY? Hey, some cats are. And there's no amount of bathing or licking or rolling around in fish heads or mouse guts that can ever fix it. You just have to embrace it, or do whatever you can to try and cover up what comes out of you.

ARE YOU PUNISHING YOUR HUMAN? If you're using your poop as a weapon, then that's a whole different kettle of fish (mmm, fish) and this entire article is moot. What are even you doing here?

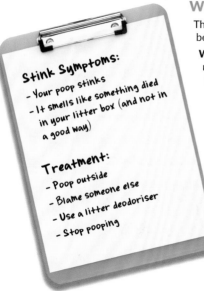

Stink Symptoms:
- Your poop stinks
- It smells like something died in your litter box (and not in a good way)

Treatment:
- Poop outside
- Blame someone else
- Use a litter deodoriser
- Stop pooping

THE PUNGE IS SO BAD. WHAT CAN I DO?

You can do plenty. Here are some suggestions:

POOP OUTSIDE Nature has a billion scents. Some are good, some are bad, and everyone just seems to accept that it's all freakin' lovely. Ergo: poop in nature.

BLAME SOMEONE ELSE This is extremely effective, but not always possible, especially if you are a lone cat. Dogs are particularly good to blame because they naturally reek of crap.

USE A LITTER DEODORISER Probably the easiest solution. Your human can sprinkle this on your litter and you don't ever have to change any habits, do any extra work or make any effort whatsoever. We like TIDY CATS Litter Tray Deodoriser (right), because it doesn't make us sneeze.

STOP POOPING This would add valuable minutes to your nap time.

MERCURY RISING

THE DAY THEY TOOK MY TEMPERATURE
...AND MY INNOCENCE

Looking back, I really should have known better. How naive I was! I went into this experiment knowing that I was putting my body out there at the mercy of humans. But I never expected it to go down this way. Or *that* way.

For those of you who don't know (or haven't yet bothered to read *My Gross Affliction, parts 1* & *2*), I, **Fred Little**, have been researching feline health and wellness. Like any good journalist, I went straight to the front lines in order to get the best possible purrspective. I mean, how better to put my paw on the pulse of veterinary science than to purrsonally experience it?

I voluntarily got in my chariot and went without struggle or complaint^ to the vet. I willingly underwent tests and examinations. I sat calmly while the stench of medicine penetrated my nostrils, all the while observing and taking mental notes. But what happened next left me feeling shocked, violated and deeply disturbed...

*See Pussweek Issue Four, available meow at pussweek.com

^I complained a little bit.

His hands were warm. Not winter-belly-warm, but tepid, like a bathmat. He was smiling down at me as he felt along my back and my neck. He checked my teef. He looked me up and down. He shone a light in my eyes and ears - he even folded one of them back to get a better look. He rubbed my glands. He listened to my heart.

In hind-leg sight I can see how incredibly creepy all of this was now. But at the time I thought I was just getting a check up. I was doing my job, you know? I was being a good cat, going above and beyond for my career as an investigative repawter, to help inform my fellow felines about good health. And to get the rabbit kibble I was promised. OK, it was mostly for the kibble.

So, there I sat on the cold metal table, trying to relax. I looked around at all the weird crap in the room. I tried not to think about what most of it was for. He picked me up and put me on the scale. He made a few crude comments about my weight and laughed. I closed my eyes and tried to think of my food bowl. I'd been gone a while. It would be worried about me. I wondered if the rabbit kibble had arrived yet, and if that jerk, Trim, was eating it.

I stepped off the scale, ready to get back in my chariot. Then suddenly Satan The Vet grabbed me, pulling me towards him. His hands moved down my back, toward my most valuable appendage - my tail. I turned and looked at him just as he yanked my tail up. Oh, the horror!

I felt the prod of cold steel. I resisted but he was holding me down. I couldn't get away! "Unhand me!" I demanded, but he wouldn't listen. I hissed, I growled, I tried to scratch, but there was nothing I could do. I had put myself in this situation (idiot!) and now I just had to sit there and take it.

It felt like an eternity, but a few seconds later it was finally over. "All good, all normal," I heard him say. HOW VERY DARE HE! There was NOTHING normal about this... this... this... PROCEDURE!

As soon as he released me from his death grip I turned and bared my claws. I went straight for the throat, but at the last second he turned and I landed on his back instead. I freaked out, jumped on the highest shelf and swore at him loudly for a solid eight minutes.

As soon as the coast was clear I made a jump for my chariot. Its door slammed shut behind me and I demanded to be escorted home at once.

I had been groped and callously man-handled... and for what?

I'm not ashamed to admit that I cried. Anyone in my situation would. On my way out I yowled as loudly as possible. I wanted the whole waiting room to hear. It was too late for me but I had to warn the other cats. The dogs not so much.

Safely back at home I wondered why this had happened to me. Of course I blamed myself. Why had I put myself through this? I had been groped and callously man-handled. He did have some pretty big callouses on those bathmat-tepid mitts of his. And for what? A few measly chunks of some delicious, succulent rabbity goodness?

My kibble! I had completely forgotten! I ran to my bowl and there it was, waiting to comfort me and make it all better. It didn't. But maybe one day, after a bit of soul searching, some hard work, and a lot more kibble, I will somehow gain the strength to move on.

Editor's note: Brave repawter Fred Little was given a generous raise for his efforts, plus extra nap time and sweet, sweet solitude. He is currently recovering in the laundry room.
PW

NOMS

MAY YOUR BOWL RUNNETH OVER

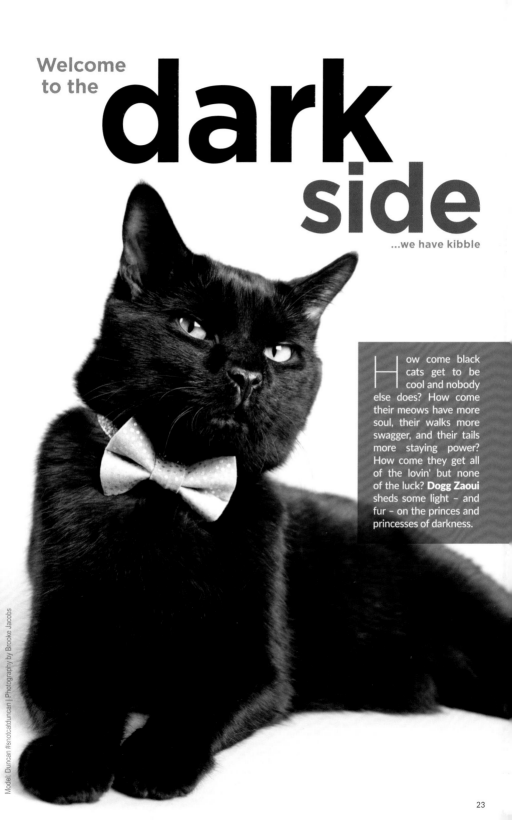

Welcome to the dark side

...we have kibble

How come black cats get to be cool and nobody else does? How come their meows have more soul, their walks more swagger, and their tails more staying power? How come they get all of the lovin' but none of the luck? **Dogg Zaoui** sheds some light – and fur – on the princes and princesses of darkness.

Model: Duncan #snotcatduncan | Photography by Brooke Jacobs

Clockwise from top: Candid pics of black cat relaxing vs. a white cat trying way too hard (and failing) to forge success in the extremely fair and nonpartisan world of modelling.

Get the luck out

Contrary to dumb-ass belief, black cats are not unlucky at all. We are, in actual fact*, the most fortuitous cats in the world. Here are just a few ways black cats are smashing the luck-o-meter:

- We're harder to take pictures of than other cats. This means that regular humans and pawparazzi don't shove their annoying cameras in our faces all that often, and the ones who do photograph us take their time and do it propurrly. So, pictures of us are much more flattering and model-esque than our dowdy white comrades - See pics (this page).

- If we actually had any flaws (which we don't), they'd be so well covered by our natural cloaks of darkness that nobody would ever see us as anything less than purrfect.

- Our delicate, sleek, liquidy flow of movement means we can silently enter and leave a room without being noticed, acknowledged or even spoken to.

- When we cross the street, moronic humans stop and walk the other way. If that isn't lucky, then I don't know what is.

*Probably

Image: Brooke Jacobs

CLAWTION: The following pages contain graphic images which some readers may find EXTREMELY disturbing. We strongly recommend that kittens, or cats prone to jumping six feet in the air, do not attempt to break the very secure seal on what can only be described as the vault of fear and darkness that lies ahead. These images are SO SCARY that we had to LICK THE PAGES SHUT for your protection, so use your claw to open them if you dare. Or don't, it's OK, nobody will judge you if you skip it. But you'll know. And you can run from this book but you can't hide from yourself, now can you? CAN YOU? No. You can't, Pussy.

If, for any reason, you are NOT traumatised forever and ever and ever by the contents of this section, then you, my furriend, are a super brave extreme courage cat. Or lion. Or lying.

PUSSWEEK EXCLUSIVE:

THE MOST
SHOCKING
TERRIFYING SCARY THINGS
IN THE WHOLE ENTIRE UNIVERSE AND BEYOND

claw here to open

MOST
SHOCKING
TERRIFYING SCARY THINGS

EXHIBIT A:

VACUUM

WHAT: They call him the cleaner. He makes problems go away. What's his problem? You are.

FEATURES: Stupid head, long neck, fat ass.

EATS: Balls, hair ties, toys, mice, tinfoil, cats.

ATTACK SEASON: Completely random. Does not discriminate based on day of the week, however will rarely strike at night.

HOW IT WILL KILL YOU: Screams at you and then sucks your brain out before ingesting you through it's long, plasticky intestine and storing your body in its musty belly.

HOW TO BEAT IT: Hide. That is all. Don't be a hero. Many cats have faced this beast and tried to bash it with their paw, only to end up deformed amputees with PTSD.

EMPTY BOWL

WHAT: A bowl which is empty can only mean one thing: There's no food in it.

FEATURES: Terrifying ceramic or solid metal, sometimes with a condescending look on its face.

EATS: All of your food, your dignity, your soul, your will to live.

ATTACK SEASON: Every goddamn day. Sometimes twice a day.

HOW IT WILL KILL YOU: Will sit and mock you, lying on the floor, empty, cold, and unapologetic as it watches you to starve to death.

HOW TO BEAT IT: Check on it at least 47 times a day. Steer your human in its direction so that they may form a shield-type barrier between you and the bowl. The bowl can be neutralised by food. Your human slave knows this, and instead of taking a bullet for you by sacrificing themselves, they simply diffuse it by pouring kibble in. But this is a temporary solution which requires ongoing maintenance.

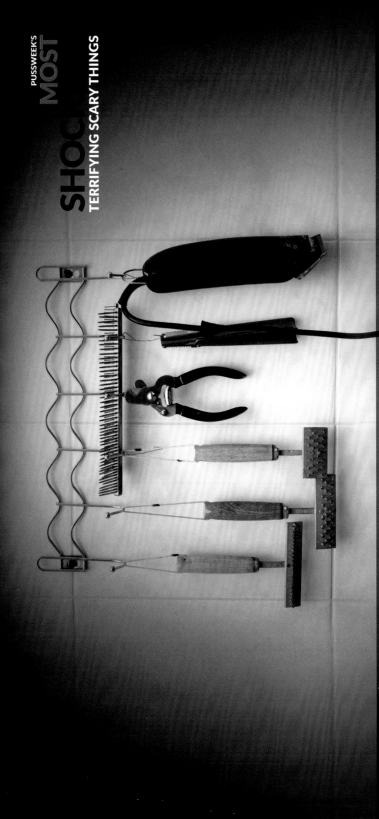

HOW THEY WILL KILL YOU: They work in conjunction with water to break your spirit and then rebuild you into an unnatural, freakish mess.

HOW TO BEAT THEM: Go full feral.

EXHIBIT E:

INSTRUMENTS OF BELITTLEMENT

WHAT: A bunch of tools that aim to steal our jobs, destroy our self respect and humiliate us.

FEATURES: Blunt teeth, sharp blades, filthy non-sterile parts covered in the fur of past victims.

EATS: Fur, skin, dignity, style.

ATTACK SEASON: Random junctures which they refer to as 'special occasions'. Sick bastards. May return regularly if especially heinous.

EXHIBIT F:

THERMOMETER

WHAT: Satan's probe.

FEATURES: Long body, tapered ice-cold burning tip.

EATS: Butts.

ATTACK SEASON: Will only strike when there is a vet around. Coincidence? We think not (see *Mercury Rising, page 20*).

HOW IT WILL KILL YOU: Makes a bee-line for the butt, and stays there until you hate yourself.

HOW TO BEAT IT: Never go to the vet. Or, hiss and bite A LOT so that it gets scared and backs off. Ollie did this once and the vet was all, "He's probably fine". Sucker.

PUSSWEEK EXCLUSIVE:

THE MOST SHOCKING

TERRIFYING SCARY THINGS

IN THE WHOLE ENTIRE UNIVERSE AND BEYOND

claw here to open

WARNING:
What lies ahead is so horrific that it might make you do a little wee. Or a big wee, depending on how much of a pussy you are. You might even poop. We're not here to make judgements about your urinary tract or bowel functions (at least not to your face). So, if you feel that you are brave enough to continue, simply claw open the following pages which we had to LICK SHUT in the interest of your safety, and let the terror wash over you.

If, for any reason, the contents of this section DO NOT leave you distressed and deeply disturbed, then you, my furriend, are truly a hero among cats. Either that, or you're full of soiled litter.

LEFTOVER
NOSE DESSERT

Crusty and delicious!

PUSSWEEK | BY CATS, FOR CATS

NEXT ISSUE

THE
BODY
ISSUE

FAT SHAMING
COULD YOU BE AT RISK?

SHAPE UP FOR
NAPPING
SEASON
FEEL LIKE A KITTEN AGAIN
WITH OUR WORKOUT TIPS

ARE YOU A HAIR-TIE
HOARDER?
WHAT ELASTICKY SECRETS ARE
HIDING UNDER YOUR COUCH?

THE HOME
STRETCH
LEG RAISES TO GET
YOUR PAWS SKY HIGH

HAIRLESS
PUSSES
THE BALD AND
THE BEAUTIFUL

THE LITTERBOX

WITH OLLIE

Need Advice? Just want to rant or say something to somebody who isn't your food bowl? PUSSWEEK's qualified* advice columnist and cat psychologist **Ollie Squishybum** is here to help.

UNIDENTIFIED SHINY OBJECT
WINNER!

Thanks to **Samuel L Catson** for sharing this special moment with us. You're the epitome of elegance and grace, and you're also the lucky winner of an **UNIDENTIFIED SHINY OBJECT**!! Congrats!!

HA HA HARDLY

Dear Ollie
I've got a HILARIOUS joke for you.
Q: What is a cat's favourite colour?
A: Brrrrrrrroooowwwwwnnn!
You're welcome. - **Alfalfa**

Dear Alfalfa
Yawn. You know what my favourite colour is? Salmon. -**Ollie**

AUDREY CRAPBURN

Dear Ollie
Look at this picture of me. Am I not the most beautiful cat in the world? Also, please look at this other picture of the wicked bomb I dropped on my human's bed! You should have heard him screaming - it was HILARIOUS!! He also cried a little bit. Probably.
- Audrey

Dear Audrey
First of all, which one is the poop? Lol jks, I think you're both beautiful. Great job on the flawless execution of what we like to call the **Duvet Poovet**. It's truly a work of art. You also win an unidentified shiny object.
-Ollie

CLEAN UP YOUR ACT

Dear Ollie
Should I pee on dirty laundry or clean laundry? And which garments are the best for my urinary flow? - **Frances**

Dear Frances
I purrsonally purrfur clean laundry, but it's not as easy to come by as the dirty stuff. Steer clear of undergarments - they've got their own problems - and instead aim for towels. They're clean even when they're dirty, and you can use the parts you haven't peed on to wrap it up like a present! Surprise! -**Ollie**

HAVE YOUR SAY AND WIN!

Send your crappy story, letter, poem, joke or photo to Ollie at litterbox@pussweekmag.com and if it makes the cut you'll definitely* WIN a SOILED^ FEATHER!!

*By 'definitely' we mean probably not. ^Soiling levels may vary. Pussweek does not accept liability for slips and falls, clumsiness, unflattering tongue-pulling faces, or dirtying of fur caused by said feather and/or soiling therein. *Ollie Squishybum assures us he got his 'degree' from Pawward Mewniversity but we haven't done any background checks. He seems pretty legit though, so we're sure it's all fine.

45

PAW READING

Dear Benji
*Here is my paw. Please look at it.- **Mocha***

Dear Mocha,
I sense that you are a black cat. I also sense that you can't commit. Only one claw is sticking out which means you want to be threatening but you really can't be bothered. Also, I sense that your paw pads are a little dry. Dip them in a cup of milk, then lick. I see a satisfying snack in your future. **-Benji**

Dear Benji,
*Here are two of my paws. Do the grey shapes beneath them mean anything important? Also, please comment on how talented I am for striking this pose. - **Tiny***

Dear Tiny,
Of all the paws I've seen in my lives, these are certainly two of them. The grey shapes are actually VERY important, because combined with the pose you are striking, this is a gang sign that means: "Tissue box potato". On an unrelated note, I see potatoes in your future. And possibly a tissue box. **-Benji**

YOUR CRYSTALS

Dear Benji
*Please look at my crystals and tell me what my future holds and what I will be in my next life. - **Lucifer***

Dear Lucifer,
You didn't even pee on these. I sense that you are a cat of very limited intelligence, with much disappointment in your future. In your next life you'll still be a cat because currently you've got about eight lives to go (if you're lucky). Then when they're all spent, you'll come back a litter crystal and hopefully, one day, live up to your purrtential. **-Benji**

FANG SHUI

Dear Benji,
*What do you think of my epic fangs? Pretty great, huh? This shot was taken right after I ate some sardines. They were delicious. - **Leroy***

Dear Leroy,
I can see from your fang formation that you have recently eaten sardines. I see a minuscule fleck of sardine lodged in there. I'd very much like to eat that fleck. You could have sent me said fleck instead of this picture, and then I'd be eating right meow, and not staring down your gross, wet gullet. **-Benji   PW**

46

Virgo (Aug 23 - Sep 22)

Virgo rhymes with bird-fro. Have you ever seen a bird with a fro? Me neither, but I sure would like to. I don't see any in your future, however I do see a shoelace. You should definitely play with it, but whatever you do, DON'T tell it any secrets.

Lucky object: Shoelace **Lucky fish:** Goldfish **Lucky bird:** Sparrow

Libra (Sep 23 - Oct 22)

Your ruling planet is not an actual planet. It's a weird, ball-shaped object which contains treats. It's a tough nut to crack but it can bring you luck if you strike at the right time. This is a not a metaphor for life. You are ruled by food. Eat up!

Lucky object: Treats **Lucky fish:** Catfish **Lucky bird:** Kookaburra

Scorpio (Oct 23 - Nov 21)

You are a fierce cat. Do you know what this means? This means you have the power to bite way more legs, ankles and toes than you currently do. Why aren't you living up to your purrtential? Go on, get chomping. Immediately. Meow.

Lucky object: Toofbrush **Lucky fish:** Iridescent shark **Lucky bird:** Swallow

Sagittarius (Nov 22 - Dec 21)

More like bad-gittarius, am I right? You're feeling reckless lately, and it's not just because of your recurring dream where you're licking the cat who lives two doors down. What are you waiting for? Get your tongue in that ear canal.

Lucky object: Computer keyboard **Lucky fish:** Atlantic Cod **Lucky bird:** Finch

Capricorn (Dec 22 - Jan 19)

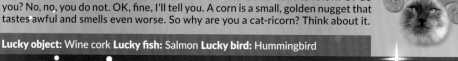

Capricorn sounds like Cat-ricorn. What is corn? You don't want to know. Or do you? No, no, you do not. OK, fine, I'll tell you. A corn is a small, golden nugget that tastes awful and smells even worse. So why are you a cat-ricorn? Think about it.

Lucky object: Wine cork **Lucky fish:** Salmon **Lucky bird:** Hummingbird

Aquarius (Jan 22 - Feb 18)

Water is great when it's *in* you, but terrible when it's *on* you. Why? Because it's water. And since you are a water sign, the same goes for you. Don't sleep ON a backpack, sleep IN it. Don't puke ON a shoe, puke IN it. Trust me.

Lucky object: Bread roll **Lucky fish:** Tuna **Lucky bird:** Seagull

Pisces (Feb 19 - Mar 20)

I'm willing to bet my last kibble that you're having litter problems right meow. Yes? Whether it's the litter you poop in, or the litter you gave birth to, something just isn't right. Fix it by sleeping in an underwear drawer every night for a week.

Lucky object: Puddle **Lucky fish:** Mackerel **Lucky bird:** Chicken

YOUR STARS

WITH BENJI

Feeling lost? Need a kick in the furry pants? PUSSWEEK's Catstrologer and Clawvoyant, **Benji**, is here to tell you what's up, read your paw, and clean up your fang shui.

Aries (Mar 21 - April 19)

Aries, they say you can't miss something you never had. But remember that time you woke up late and missed breakfast and starved to death? Or what about that time you missed a spot while bathing and your fur stank of human? Exactly.

Lucky object: Chicken nugget **Lucky fish:** Koi **Lucky bird:** Duck

Taurus (Apr 20 - May 20)

You're so pretty. You're the prettiest of all the cats. And you're special. So special, in fact, that you deserve a gigantic cardboard castle with corrugated floors and claw holes in the roof. So pack your bags, it's time to move. An inch to the left.

Lucky object: Bag of sand **Lucky fish:** Siamese fighting fish **Lucky bird:** Goose

Gemini (May 21 - Jun 20)

What nobody ever tells you is that dogs smell. But that's because it's obvious, right? Wrong. Did you know that some cats like the smell of dog? And their noses work and everything. All I'm saying is, dogs smell. They really, really smell.

Lucky object: Caterpillar **Lucky fish:** Perch **Lucky bird:** Cockatoo

Cancer (Jun 21 - Jul 22)

Twinkle twinkle little star, how I wonder what you are. I also wonder what the hell you're doing up there, staring down at me creepily from a gazillion miles away. What's your deal, seriously? Oh, Cancer, hi... Uhh, fish in your future, etc.

Lucky object: Disposable coffee cup **Lucky fish:** Barracuda **Lucky bird:** Magpie

Leo (Jul 23 - Aug 22)

Your aura is especially hairy lately, and if you're not careful this can lead to emotional hairballs. Cleanse your soul with some top-of-the-wardrobe dust and a pinch of sock lint, then shred a silk shirt and/or tweed jacket for good luck.

Lucky object: Sandal **Lucky fish:** Carp **Lucky bird:** Penguin

MO' PUSS?
NO PAWBLEM

YEP, WE'VE GOT ISSUES. MORE PUSSWEEK AVAILABLE MEOW!

COLLECT THEM ALL AT PUSSWEEK.COM

BUB FACTS

BUB'S BOD

BUB has an extreme case of dwarfism, which means her limbs are disproportionately small in relation to the rest of her body, and she has some difficulty moving around. She has short, stubby legs and a long body.

BUB'S AN ETERNAL KITTEN

BUB is a "perma-kitten", which means she will stay kitten-sized and maintain kitten-like features her entire life.

BUB TOES THE LINE

BUB is a polydactyl cat, meaning she has extra toes, and in her case, one extra toe on all of her four paws, adding up to 22 toes (and 22 claws)!

BUB'S IN THE LOOP

Shortly after turning one year old, BUB was diagnosed with an exceptionally rare bone condition called osteopetrosis. BUB is the only cat in recorded history to have been born with this disease, which has made it very difficult to treat. She meow uses a device called the **Assisi Loop**, which uses Pulsed Electromagnetic Field Therapy. Since starting these treatments, BUB is able to run and jump like never before – something she was told would never happen!

TRAVEL BUB

BUB is always calm, and surprisingly comfortable and at peace in just about any situation. She loves to travel and gladly sits on her human's lap in cabs, subways, planes and even on his shoulder as he walks around outside. **PW**

BUB, QUEEN OF NOMS

BUB's lower jaw is significantly shorter than her upper jaw, and her teeth never grew in which is why her tongue is always hanging around. Fortunately BUB has a very healthy appetite and eats dry and wet food with no problems! Phew!

BUB facts from lilbub.com | Photographs courtesy of Mike Bridavsky

I've noticed that you're extremely chilled. What's your secret to being so tolerant?

I don't have much to be tolerant of (well, other than my brother, Spooky). But other than that, I am deeply grateful for my quality of life. The secret to my serenity lies deep within a meteor many light years away. It's really hard to explain.

BUB, your tongue is arguably your best asset. How do you keep it so moist and shiny, considering its tendency to protrude?

Saliva.

Do you have any problems bathing? What's your licking style?

I can't always reach the stinkiest parts of my body, but I get help with that. My licking style could be described as "obsessively ineffective".

Have you ever inadvertently picked up something tasty (or not-so-tasty) on your tongue by mistake?

Most definitely I have. Let's just say I don't use clumping litter!

What is the best perk that comes from being a famous interweb cat?

I actually prefer not to be referred to as an "interweb cat", mostly because I'm scared of spiders. But I can comment on the perks of fame, the biggest one being that humans are especially nice to you.

What is the hardest part of being this fabulous?

Being amazing is really easy for me, it's totally effortless.

Do you ever long for the days of normalcy, when you can lick your butt in peace?

There is an assumption that my life is not normal, but the truth is that my life is quite normal to me (even though it has never involved licking my butt, or anyone else's for that matter). What I hope for are the days when we can all celebrate our own differences, as well as each other's.

What do you do for fun? What's your guilty pleasure?

I love to nap, eat, and meditate. And while I don't know what a guilty pleasure is, I can say that I find great pleasure in a fine yoghurt or a stinky fish!

What tips would you give regular house cats who are dreaming of star-studded greatness?

I don't think that any regular house cats dream of star-studded greatness. What I do know is that they dream of long naps, rolling balls of yarn, tender snuggles, and a warm and safe place to call home. My dream is that their dreams come true.

How many hours a day do you sleep? Does your sleep schedule ever suffer because of your job?

My job is to sleep, so my sleep schedule actually benefits because of my job.

Being successful is a lot of work. Do you do all of it yourself or do you have help?

Being successful can certainly be a lot of work for some folks, yes. But I actually don't do much at all other than deep meditation, some occasional energy healing, and of course digesting food can be quite tiring if you eat enough.

"Being amazing is really easy for me, it's totally effortless"

Photo by William Winchester Claytor

BUB, How long did it take you to get this popular, and how did you do it?

There is this preconceived notion that I had to rise to popularity (that's how your society works, I understand that now). But I've actually always been wildly popular, it's just been a matter of people finally realising it. There are still thousands of people that realise how popular I am every day.

Do you think your disability hinders you in any way? What are your limitations?

It seems as though you might be referring to my slow adaptation to your planet's exceptionally strong gravitational field. It's true, it's certainly impacted my mobility, but at the same time it's greatly enhanced my other senses and abilities. For example, my [clawvoyant] strength, telepathic precision, and telekinetic accuracy have never been more finely tuned. But I do have a hard time moving about, and sometimes I step in my poop.

A slip of the **tongue**

L il **BUB**. More like lil BABE, am I right? Yes, yes, I am. Those eyes, those socks, that tongue... Dayummmmmm, girl! But beyond her good looks, BUB is exceptionally intelligent, caring, and an all-round good cat. She's different, you know? She cares. Does that make her a cat still? Fortunately for us felines, yes. Yes, it does.

An advocate for homeless and special needs animals all over the universe, BUB encourages adoptions and helps those less fortunate. She's an unstoppable force - radiating positivity, chill, inspiration and acceptance (yes, we're sure she's a cat - we checked).

What's the catch, you ask? Well, she does claim to be from outer space. But you know, that's OK because one time I claimed I was a cabbage and I spent the whole day on the kitchen bench, waiting to transform into a spring roll. But unlike that identity crisis, BUB's claim to extra-terrestrial breedership might just be verifiable - after all, no regular earth cat could be as purrfect as she is.

So read on, dear felines, because I, **Ollie Squishybum**, was lucky enough to talk to her and ask her questions about things. I promised myself I wouldn't fall in love. I failed. Hard.

Are you
being stalked
for interweb fame & gain?

There's one way to find out. Well, actually, there are several ways to find out, but this is the best way. Probably. Answer these questions by circling yes or no:

Does your human follow you around?	yes	no
Is your human constantly calling your name and making squeaky and/or kissy noises?	yes	no
Do you have a fone or camera shoved in your face on a regular basis?	yes	no
Have you ever received mysterious fan mail from cats you don't know?	yes	no
Do cats throw themselves at you for no apparent reason (other than the obvious, of course)?	yes	no
Do you regularly receive extravagant gifts/treats/ meowchandise which you are then photographed using/ eating/wearing?	yes	no
Are you constantly under pressure to 'give the people what they want'?	yes	no
Are your naps ever cut short for 'camera time'?	yes	no
Have you ever heard a clicking noise while you're licking your butt?	yes	no
Do you ever get the feeling someone is watching you (other than damn dirty ceiling bugs)?	yes	no

Were the majority of your answers yes or no?

Yes. What meow?

Do you enjoy being famous? Are you happy and relaxed, or are you stressed and upset? If you're having fun, then live it up, baby! Eat all the treats, lap up all the luxury! But if for any reason you're unhappy, start sharpening your claws and planning an escape route. You've only got nine lives, so live them for yourself and nobody else, do you hear me? Do you? DO YOU? Good.

No. What meow?

You're free to go. Return to your nap. Good day. **PW**

STARS WE LOVE
Ninja

NINJA

BREED Domestic House Panther

OCCUPATION Full-time model, biscuit maker, treat taster

GUILTY PLEASURE Cuddling

Ninja

FAVE THING ABOUT BEING FAMOUS Meeting new friends, showing off how great us black kitties can be, and all the treats I get for modeling, of course!

HOT TIP FOR CATS WANTING TO BECOME FAMOUS Be yourself! Figure out what your talent is & stick with it!

WORDS OF WISDOM / QUOTE TO LIVE BY You can't live a full life on an empty stomach!

PLATFORMS 📷 @ninja_poofy_ittybitty

Images courtesy of @ninja_poofy_ittybitty

YEEZY

BREED Domestic Shorthair

OCCUPATION Model & Blogger

GUILTY PLEASURE Whipped cream

Yeezy

HOW DID YOU BECOME FAMOUS?
Just being myself. Not to toot my own horn but I'm pretty awesome. Toot! Toot!

HOT TIP FOR CATS WANTING TO BECOME FAMOUS
My best tip is to post pics daily. Everyone wants to see your cute face!

WORDS OF WISDOM / QUOTE TO LIVE BY
Real Hip Hop is not on the radio

PLATFORMS  @yeezycat

Images courtesy of @yeezycat

STARS WE LOVE
Yeezy

STARS WE LOVE
Toothless

TOOTHLESS

BREED Bombay

OCCUPATION Part-time supermodel

GUILTY PLEASURE
10-hour beauty naps

Toothless

FAVE THING ABOUT BEING FAMOUS
It's always great when we can help out some furry friends in need. That's the part I like most!

HOT TIP FOR CATS WANTING TO BECOME FAMOUS
Get a good manager

WORDS OF WISDOM / QUOTE TO LIVE BY
I'm not purrfect, I'm original.

PLATFORMS 📷 @toothlesstheblack.cat

Images courtesy of @toothlesstheblack.cat

Cola

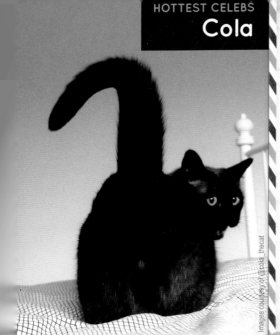

COLA

BREED Siamese x Ragdoll

OCCUPATION Model

GUILTY PLEASURE
I love to dance, you'll see a lot of my dancing pics online!

HOW DID YOU BECOME FAMOUS?
I slowly gained more followers since I started posting pics of my fine self on Instagram!

FAVE THING ABOUT BEING FAMOUS
Having so many friends

LEAST FAVE THING ABOUT BEING FAMOUS
The pawparazzi taking pictures of me every day

HOT TIP FOR CATS WANTING TO BE FAMOUS
Looks don't matter, just be a little crazy and different and anyone can become famous

WORDS OF WISDOM / QUOTE TO LIVE BY
Eat, sleep, dance, repeat!

PLATFORMS

  @cola_thecat

Cola

Images courtesy of @cola_thecat

LOVER BOY

BREED British Shorthair

OCCUPATION Influencer/Furlanthropist

GUILTY PLEASURE I love obtaining strands of dried spaghetti and hiding them under the rug. I once made it to 18 strands before my lair was rumbled. It is now suspected I am hiding them behind the litter box. I can neither confirm nor deny.

HOW DID YOU BECOME FAMOUS? Rampant over-sharing of my day-to-day activities. Also: chiseled features

FAVE THING ABOUT BEING FAMOUS
Being able to use my fame to promote charitable causes, like the charitable cause of my mouth needing meatballs.

LEAST FAVE THING ABOUT BEING FAMOUS
Constant public scrutiny of my curvaliciousness. It's called a primordial pouch, guys! Google it!

HOT TIP FOR CATS WANTING TO BE FAMOUS
Stay true to your roots.

WORDS OF WISDOM / QUOTE TO LIVE BY An unattended block of parmesan not licked is an opportunity missed!

PLATFORMS @loverboy.brit

Lover Boy

Lover Boy

Images courtesy of @loverboy.brit

Felix & Logan

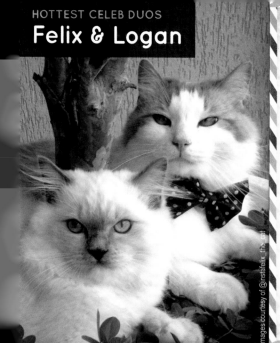

FELIX & LOGAN

BREED Ragdoll

OCCUPATION
Kings of the castle

GUILTY PLEASURE
Car riding! We love
to ride like dogs, feeling
the wind on our whiskers!

HOW DID YOU BECOME FAMOUS?
Being adorable and not looking at the camera

FAVE THING ABOUT BEING FAMOUS
Getting paid with treats

LEAST FAVE THING ABOUT BEING FAMOUS
Humans recording everything we do

MOST ATHLETIC
Logan (consistent winner in the 3am house race)

SMARTEST/WISEST
Felix (opens doors, steals from kitchen cupboard)

HOT TIP FOR CATS WANTING TO BE FAMOUS
Be yourself! Do whatever you like!

PLATFORMS @instafelix_the_cat

Images courtesy of @instafelix_the_cat

EVEY & TOTO

BREED
Evey: Calico/Maine Coon
Toto: Scottish Fold

OCCUPATION
Evey: Full-Time Princess,
avid string enthusiast
Toto: Resting-shocked-face champion,
Chief of head butts

GUILTY PLEASURE Rolling around in catnip.

HOW DID YOU BECOME FAMOUS?
Toto: I sit like a human and cross my paws

LEAST FAVE THING ABOUT BEING FAMOUS
Not being able to give pawtographs

MOST LIKELY TO SPOT A BUG ON THE CEILING FIRST
Evey (also the bravest & least lazy one)

MOST LIKELY TO FALL IN THE TOILET BOWL
Toto (super big clutz who runs into glass all the time)

HOT TIP FOR CATS WANTING TO BE FAMOUS
Just be yourself and purrfect that pose!

PLATFORMS @evey_and_toto

Images courtesy of @evey_and_toto

Evey & Toto

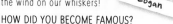

Cole, you were a lone cat for a while. How did you feel when Marmalade first showed up?

C: At first I wasn't too sure about this little ginger thing, but soon realised it was great fun having a brother to play with and to take part in kitty olympics at 3am!

You're best known as a team. Do either of you think you would have become this famous if the other one wasn't in the picture?

M: I don't think we would have been as famous if we weren't a team since we get up to so much fun playing together. Our most popular videos are the ones of us exploring new things and our reactions towards one another.

Is there any news on your love lives?

M: We're indoor kitties and haven't met any other cats, although we once saw a very attractive lady cat at the vet one time. That definitely made the visit a little better...

Do either of you have any illegitimate kittens?

C: Nope we're both neutered and no longer have our trouble nuggets!

Marm, how is the relationship meow between you and *that* money box?

M: Now that my human has explained to me that it isn't a real cat, I'm fine with it...

Between the two of you, which one is:

The funny one?

C: We both have our moments, Marm is definitely the goofiest.

M: Cole can be just as goofy, although he's the oldest and apparently the wisest.

The cleanest one?

M: Definitely me. Cole gets litter butt-nuggets. It's hilarious, but can be very distracting.

The smoochiest one?

C: Definitely me, I'm the biggest snuggler between us.

M: I used to save my snuggles exclusively for the toilet, but lately I'm slowly becoming more of a lap cat outside of the bathroom. It's warmer.

What's the worst thing about being famous?

M: Not knowing we were famous until meow! I will demand more boxes and cat treats immediately!!

What advice would you give to cats who are dreaming of interweb fame?

C: Try to "perform" for your humans when they are filming you. We know your immediate instinct is to do the opposite to what they want and ignore them, but you won't get famous that way! It's hard, but worth it!

Images courtesy of Chris Poole

COLE & MARMALADE

BREED
Cole: Unknown, possibly some Turkish Angora
Marmalade: Ginger Tabby Shorthair

Cole

Marmalade

OCCUPATION
Cole: Therapist
Marmalade: Comeowdian

WORDS OF WISDOM / QUOTE TO LIVE BY
Cole: Stay Pawsitive!
Marmalade: Never give up, never surrender!

PLATFORMS
 @coleandmarmalade

WEBSITE + SHOP
coleandmarmalade.com

HOTTEST CELEB DUOS
Cole & Marmalade

Images courtesy of Chris Poole

Cole and Marmalade, can either of you pin-point the moment you became famous? Was it gradual or did it hit you in the face like a wet leaf?

M: What... We're famous?!

C: It was gradual, our human has been making videos of us and posting to our social sites for 5 years now, although many of our first videos were popular and went viral. I think it was after Marmalade came along that our popularity really skyrocketed and we were officially cat celebrities!

How did you become so popular? Did your human slaves do all the work?

Obviously we have pawesome purrsonalities and we're very cute and fun to watch... But our human servants did most of the work. We're mostly too busy napping to help and we'd rather sleep on the computer than do work on it.

Cole, you are a black cat by trade, and a beautiful one at that. How do you keep your coat so glossy and silky smooth?

C: I groom a minimum of an hour daily, Marm helps too. Then we take coconut oil daily, which really gives our coats that glossy shine.

Do either of you ever feel discriminated against because of your colouring?

C: I know our human started making videos about me in the first place because black cats are the last to be adopted and first to be euthanised in animal shelters because of the stigma surrounding us, so yes, I feel that black cats get a bad rap form these silly folklores from centuries ago.

M: Nope.

Izzy & The Fluff

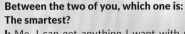

How did you become famous?
We guess our human servant takes some nice pictures of us with that weird clicky thing, while we are just being cute and adorable as always.

Best part of being famous?
I: Famous? What's that? Can we eat it?

Worst part of being famous?
I: Apparently we can't eat it.
Z: But in all seriousness, yeah, we can't eat it.

THE IZZY & ZOE (a.k.a. THE FLUFF)

BREED 1/2 British, 1/2 European Shorthair, except Zoe does not conform to the rules of shorthair and became The Fluff instead

OCCUPATION
Izzy: Full-time owl impressionist and purrfessional cuddler
Zoe: Queen Of Hearts and Honorary Care Bear

PLATFORMS

@izzyandthefluff

WEBSITE
izzyandthefluff.com

Izzy

Zoe (the Fluff)

Between the two of you, which one is:
The smartest?
I: Me. I can get anything I want with my wide-eyed innocent face and on point head-tilt, but make no mistake, I know exactly what I am doing.

The clumsy one?
Z: My extreme curiosity might cause me to stumble and fall (in the full bathtub) sometimes.

Which of you is most likely to fall in love with an inanimate object?
Z: I am in love with anything that is made of plastic. It's a forbidden love – my humans will never let me chew on it. Something about being unhealthy. Whatever. I'll never abandon my love.

What do you do for fun? What's your guilty pleasure?
I: I like to catch and eat crunchy bugs.
Z: I like to do random side-jumps against walls and furniture. Also, I like to bitch slap plants for no apparent reason. They know what they did.

Hot tip for regular house cats wanting to become famous?
Instruct your humans to buy a real clicky thing, not that fone thing they are always using. Our cuteness deserves to be captured in the maximum resolution.

Words of wisdom / quote to live by:
You can never go wrong with a tuxedo.

Sophie The Model

Sophie, you are a purrfessional model. How do you stay in shape and keep your coat so glossy?

I try to eat right, having 15-16 small meals throughout the day and night. I'm not one of those cats that can do that 'cotton ball soaked in tuna water' diet – I need real food! And treats! Give me treats!! I guess I just have a fast metabolism to keep the weight off, but I do enjoy running away from my human a few times a day. The healthy diet keeps my fur shiny and bouncy too.

When did you become famous?

I think that I was famous from the moment that I was born, I just needed everyone to finally open their eyes and realise it! Humans tend to be a little slow in the reality department sometimes.

What are the best and worst things about being a famous cat?

The best thing is being able to use my platform to help other kitties in need and to make them smile. And swag. Yeah, definitely swag. The worst thing is that I always have to be "on". I rarely get a day off to just relax in the closet.

How often do you bathe?

Listen, I never know when the pawparazzi is going to be shoving a camera in my face so I am CONSTANTLY keeping myself well groomed and smelling spitty. It'll be that one time that I have a cobweb in my whiskers that will end up on the cover of a magazine if I'm not careful.

Do you smooch?

I'm not much of a smoocher. When my sister Madeline was alive, I would smooch with her, but nobody else. Everyone has bad breath,

and besides, I don't want to mess up my beautiful pouty lips.

Your lips? Cats don't have lips.

Sticks tongue out

Uhh, I don't know what that means, but you're incredibly pretty and I just forgot my own name there for a second, so I'm going to move on with the questions meow. Have you ever been caught drinking water from the toilet bowl?

Seriously?! I'll leave that disgusting behavior for the lowlife D.O.G. I only drink bottled water from my filtered fountain or fresh rainwater from my chalice that I keep outside.

How do you respond to claims that you were caught on camera exposing your belly to a flea-riddled stray?

LIES! ALL LIES! He was a legitimate furtographer from Spain! Just because he had long hair doesn't mean that he had fleas. The press like to sensationalise everything for a good story!

What advice would you give to cats who are dreaming of interweb fame?

Always look your best, amuse the humans by letting them take your photo, and just be real! Don't put on a show - be yourself and let your purrsonality shine through. People don't want to just see a pretty face, they want to connect with your purrsonality!

SOPHIE THE MODEL

BREED
1/2 Russian Blue,
1/2 Black Awesome

OCCUPATION
Purrfessional Model,
Black Cat Ambassador

PLATFORMS

🅾 🅕 🅨 @sophie_the_model

WEBSITE sophiethecatmodel.com

Sophie

Images courtesy of @sophie_the_model

Lurking human, hidden camera

It's happening all over the world: A simple tabby is just doing his thing, minding his own business, then casually decides to stick his head through a hole in a slice of bread. No big deal, right? Wrong. One day, a few months later, that same tabby falls asleep on a computer keyboard and awakes to find his picture is all over the interweb! He's famous! But how? I'll tell you how: HIS HUMAN SECRETLY FILMED HIM, THEN POSTED IT ONLINE!! And the worst part is this is way more common than we think.

Many of us - even you - might be on display right meow. If you've ever sat with your legs akimbo, if you've left your toe beans exposed, if you've ever been furry on a Friday, or stuck your tongue out on a Tuesday, then you could be at serious risk of purrblic exposure.

But is it all bad? Believe it or not, some cats actually enjoy it. They know they're being photographed and they lap it up like double cream. Some of them even pose. And they're smart, too - they've found ways to use their fame to help cats in need, and get armies of humans working for them.

So how does an ordinary, everyday house cat become an elite member of the litterati? Pussweek's entertainment repawter **Pachinko** talks to some of social meowdia's biggest celebrities to get the low-down on the world of not-so-accidental interweb fame.

SPOTTED!

We caught actor **Furgus Furrybits** being meowed at by his overbearing mother on top of a nearby fence!

SPOTTED!

Blowing the lid off recent pregnancy rumours, **Nutella Portici** was spotted sunning her soon-to-be-lactating nipples on a crusty old slab of concrete!

D1291581

NOTHIN' BUT NET

ABOVE & LEFT: We snapped **Kobe Foursocks** interrogating some seedy looking fish at the infamous South Wharf last week. When confronted, Foursocks denied any shady business dealings, pointing out the clear lack of trees in the area. This is not the first time Foursocks has been caught in the company of fishy characters – just a few months ago he was picked up for torturing a family of cod down at the grotty pier.

TEXTURAL HEELING

RIGHT: Food model **Greyjoy** looked more than a little guilty when we caught him pawing at a pair of shoes yesterday. He was noticeably flustered as he adamantly denied trying them on, informing us that he was simply feeling them out so that he could pee in them later. In a conflicting statement, he then told us that the texture of the supple leather was good for his SPS (Sensitive Paw Syndrome) a disease which we're pretty sure he made up.